LITTLE & **Large**

Sticker Activity

STICKY HISTORY

Miles Kelly

First published in 2006 by Miles Kelly Publishing Ltd
Bardfield Centre, Great Bardfield, Essex, CM7 4SL, UK

Copyright © Miles Kelly Publishing Ltd 2006

This edition printed in 2010

2 4 6 8 10 9 7 5 3 1

Editorial Director Belinda Gallagher
Art Director Jo Brewer
Assistant Editors Amanda Askew, Lucy Dowling, Hannah Todd
Designer Tom Slemmings
Cover Designer Simon Lee
Production Manager Elizabeth Brunwin
Reprographics Anthony Cambray, Ian Paulyn
Assets Manager Bethan Ellish

ISBN 978-1-84810-244-6

Printed in China

British Library Cataloguing-in-Publication Data
A catalogue record for this book is available from the British Library

All images from the Miles Kelly Archives

Made with paper from a sustainable forest

www.mileskelly.net
info@mileskelly.net

www.factsforprojects.com
The one-stop homework helper — pictures, facts, videos, projects and more

Ancient Egypt

With magnificent pyramids and amazing tombs that can still be seen today, ancient Egypt is an important part of history.

Not only did the ancient Egyptians create breathtaking buildings, they also invented lots of useful things such as a kind of paper called papyrus and a form of picture-writing called hieroglyphics.

With this great sticker book you can learn all about the lives of ancient Egyptians and impress your friends with amazing facts!

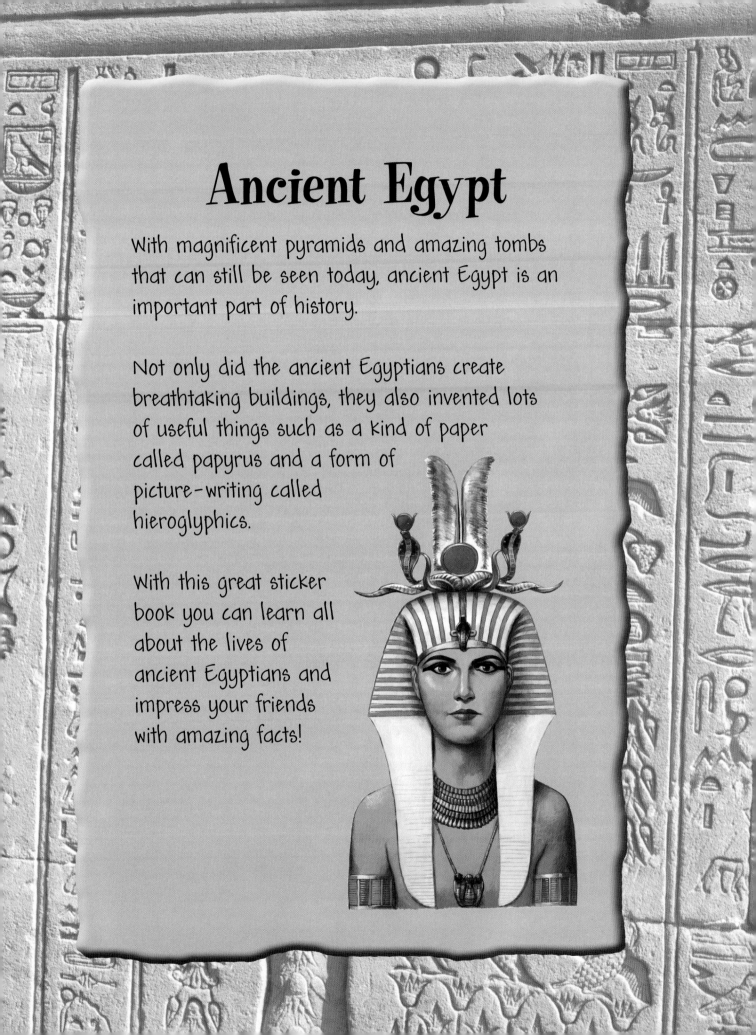

Mini stickers!

How did ancient Egyptians build their magnificent buildings? Who were the most powerful people? How was paper made? Use your mini stickers to learn all about ancient Egyptians and their daily life.

Monuments – important structures, such as pyramids

Rulers – the great rulers of Egypt, including queens and pharaohs

Jobs – who's who in ancient Egypt, from farmers to doctors

Gods and goddesses – gods and goddesses worshipped by the ancient Egyptians

Pictures and words – making paper, ink and picture-writing

Monuments

▲ Step pyramid

▲ Temple at Abu Simbel

▲ The Great Pyramid

▲ The Great Sphinx

▲ The Great Hall at Karnak

▲ Lighthouse at Alexandria

Rulers

▲ Ramses II

► Pharaoh Pepi II

▲ Queen Cleopatra VII

▲ Amenhotep IV

▲ Queen Hatshepsut

▲ Tutankhamun

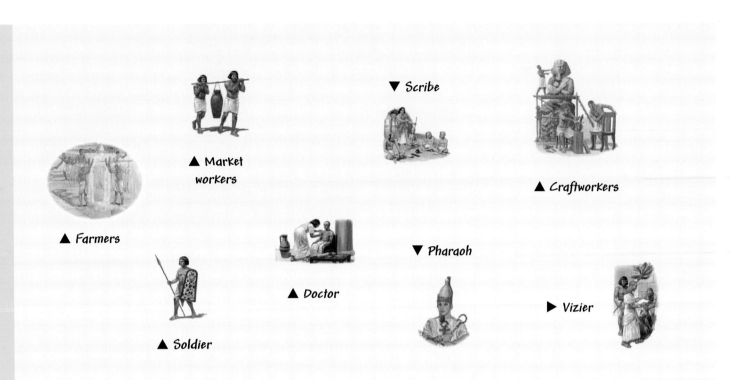

▲ Market workers

▼ Scribe

▲ Craftworkers

▲ Farmers

▲ Doctor

▼ Pharaoh

▶ Vizier

▲ Soldier

▲ Bes

◀ Sobek

▲ Thoth

▶ Ra

▲ Bastet

▲ Horus

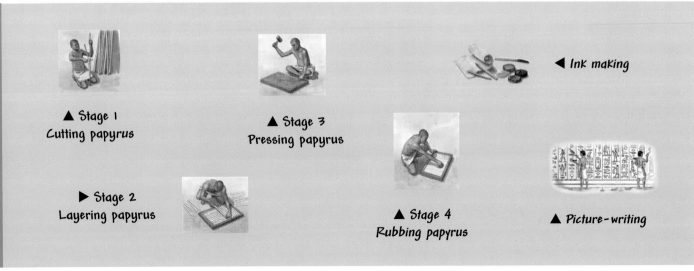

▲ Stage 1
Cutting papyrus

▲ Stage 3
Pressing papyrus

◀ Ink making

▶ Stage 2
Layering papyrus

▲ Stage 4
Rubbing papyrus

▲ Picture-writing

Ancient Egypt

 ◄ **Ramses II**
Ruling for over 60 years, Ramses II was a great builder and a brave soldier

 ► **Pharaoh**
The pharaoh was the most important and powerful person in Egypt – he ruled the country

 ▼ **Farmers**
Most people were farmers, mainly growing wheat and barley

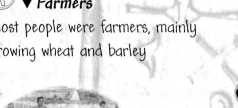

 ▲ **Bastet**
The goddess of cats, musicians and dancers – cats were holy animals and treated very well

 ▲ **The Great Pyramid**
Made from over two million blocks of limestone, it was built a burial place for King Khufu

 ► **The Great Sphinx**
Guarding the way to the Great Pyramid, this huge statue has the body of a lion and the head of a man

 ▲ **Pharaoh Pepi II**
He became king at only six years old and reigned for 94 years – the longest reign in history

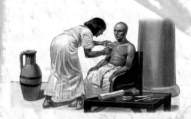

 ◄ **Doctor**
Egyptian doctors used medicines made from plants

KEY:

Monuments

Rulers

Jobs

Gods and goddesses

Pictures and words

◄ Stage 2
Layering papyrus
The strips of papyrus were placed onto a frame to make layers

▲ Stage 1
Cutting papyrus
Papyrus reeds grew on the banks of the river Nile and were used to write on – at first they had to be cut into lots of thin strips

▲ Stage 3
Pressing papyrus
The strips were pressed to squeeze out the water and squash the layers together

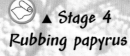

▲ Stage 4
Rubbing papyrus
When the papyrus was dry, the surface was rubbed with a stone to make it smooth for writing on

▼ Queen Hatshepsut
During her reign, Queen Hatshepsut sent five ships to Punt, on the coast of the Red Sea, which brought back many valuable goods

▲ Bes
Families worshipped the god of children and the home

► Sobek
The god of the river Nile, Sobek kept crocodiles in a pool next to his temples

▲ Soldier
Soldiers carried metal spears and shields made of wood or ox hide

Temple visitors had to shave off their hair and eyebrows before they were allowed to enter these holy buildings!

Building pyramids

Pyramids were large tombs (burial places) for kings and pharaohs. The pyramids at the town of Giza were built for three kings and are more than 4500 years old. The Great Pyramid took over 20 years to build and is about 140 metres high. Each block weighed as much as two and a half adult elephants!

Finished pyramids had a special white coating to protect the stones

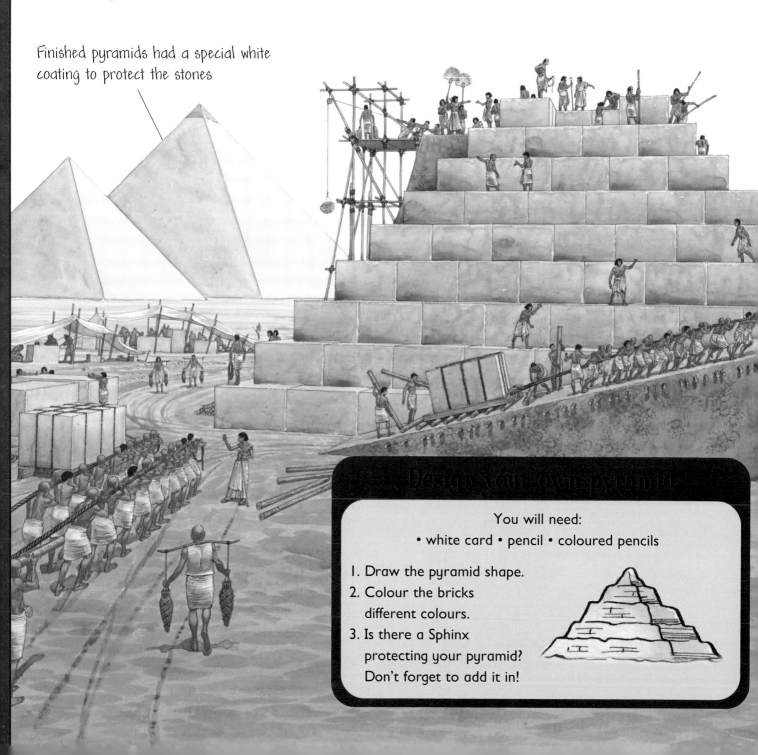

Design your own pyramid

You will need:
• white card • pencil • coloured pencils

1. Draw the pyramid shape.
2. Colour the bricks different colours.
3. Is there a Sphinx protecting your pyramid? Don't forget to add it in!

Ancient Egypt

▲ The Great Sphinx

▲ Bastet

▲ Pharaoh Pepi II

▲ The Great Pyramid

▲ Doctor

▲ Ramses II

▲ Pharaoh

▲ Farmers

▲ The Great Sphinx

► Bastet

◄ Pharaoh Pepi II

▲ The Great Pyramid

▲ Doctor

◄ Ramses II

▲ Pharaoh

► Farmers

Ancient Egypt

▲ Stage 1
Cutting papyrus

▲ Stage 2
Layering papyrus

▲ Stage 3
Pressing papyrus

▲ Stage 4
Rubbing papyrus

▲ Soldier

▲ Queen Hatshepsut

▲ Sobek

▲ Bes

◀ Stage 1
Cutting
papyrus

▼ Stage 2
Layering papyrus

▶ Stage 3
Pressing
papyrus

▶ Stage 4
Rubbing
papyrus

◀ Soldier

◀ Queen
Hatshepsut

◀ Sobek

▶ Bes

◀ Queen Cleopatra VII

▲ Amenhotep IV

▼ Scribe

▲ Lighthouse at Alexandria

▲ Picture-writing

▶ Thoth

▲ Temple at Abu Simbel

▼ Ink making

▲ Queen Cleopatra VII

▲ Amenhotep IV

▲ Scribe

▲ Lighthouse at Alexandria

▲ Picture-writing

▲ Thoth

▲ Ink making

▲ Temple at Abu Simbel

Ancient Egypt

▲ Tutankhamun

▼ The Great
Hall at Karnak

▲ Ra

▼ Horus

▲ Vizier

▲ Craftworkers

▼ Step pyramid

▲ Market workers

▲ Ra

▲ Tutankhamun

▲ The Great
Hall at Karnak

▲ Vizier

▲ Craftworkers

▲ Horus

▲ Step pyramid

▲ Market workers

Making mummies

Ancient Egyptians believed that when someone died, they travelled to another world. They needed their bodies for this, so they were made into mummies. Making mummies was very hard work. First, all the organs except the heart were removed, including the brain, stomach and lungs. Then the body was covered in salt and dried for 40 days. Next, the body was washed and stuffed with linen so it would keep its shape. Finally, it was oiled and wrapped in lots of linen bandages. A death mask, made of gold and precious stones, was fitted over the mummy's face to help the dead person's spirit recognize the mummy.

The priest in charge wore a jackal mask to represent the god Anubis.

Mummy

Wooden coffin for the body

Make a mummy mask

You will need:
- play mask • PVA glue • newspaper • white paint
- paintbrush • poster paints • glitter

1. Cover the mask with a thick layer of PVA glue.
2. Spread layers of torn newspaper strips over the mask and leave to dry.
3. Cover the mask with white paint.
4. Decorate your mask with poster paint and glitter.

Ancient Egypt

▲ **Temple at Abu Simbel**
Four huge statues of Ramses II guard the temple's entrance

◀ **Thoth**
Egyptians thought hieroglyph came from Thoth, the moon g who usually had the head of ibis (a kind of bird)

◀ **Scribe**
Scribes were important people because they recorded everything that happened – they also taught their sons to be scribes

▼ **Amenhotep IV**
During his reign, Amenhotep made the sun god, Ra, king of the gods

▲ **Lighthouse at Alexandria**
One of the Seven Wonders of the Ancient World, Pharos, the first ever lighthouse, protected the harbours at Alexandria

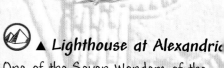

▲ **Ink making**
Ink was made using water with soot, charcoal or coloured minerals

▶ **Queen Cleopatra VII**
Cleopatra was one of the last rulers of Egypt and married Roman general, Mark Anthony

▲ **Picture-writing**
Artists used picture-writing to decorate tombs – this was called hieroglyphics

KEY:

 Monuments

 Rulers

 Jobs

 Gods and goddesses

 Pictures and words

▼ Horus

...s god was the
...tector of the pharaoh,
... Egyptians wore a
...ky charm, the eye of
...us, to protect them

◄ Craftworkers

Craftworkers built statues
and furniture for the
pharaoh and they often
had their own areas within
the town to work

▲ Step pyramid

The world's oldest kind of
pyramids, they were built
like giant staircases

► Market workers

These workers are carrying
oil to market – they could
exchange it for anything,
even food

▼ Vizier

Viziers helped the
pharaoh run the
country – they were
very important

► Ra

As the sun god, he was the
most important god of all –
he later became Amun-Ra,
the king of the gods

▲ Tutankhamun

The boy-king
Tutankhamun's death mask
was found in the Valley of
Kings about 80 years ago

► The Great Hall at Karnak

Built by Ramses II, the Great Hall
at Karnak has 134 papyrus columns
up to 21 metres tall

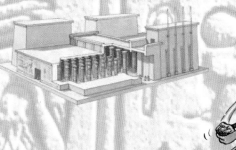

To protect their crops, Egyptian farmers hired young boys to scare away the
birds. They needed to have a very loud voice and a good aim with a slingshot!

The biggest and best!

Every year, the river Nile flooded the land between July and November.

Egyptians wore lucky charms called amulets, which were meant to protect them from evil spirits.

Egyptians wrote on papyrus – at first on long strips, but later in books. Papyrus is long lasting and has been known to survive for up to 3000 years!

Read on to find out about some ancient record-breaking facts

• Animals were made into mummies, too. Cats and dogs were often mummified and buried with their owners. One mummified crocodile discovered was over 4.5 metres long.

• Ramses II was the only pharaoh to carry the title 'the Great' after his name. He had a huge number of children – 96 boys and 60 girls!

• The Egyptian alphabet was made up of a system called hieroglyphics – there were 700 hieroglyhics in total. Some of the symbols stood for sounds and some for words.

E
G
Y
P
T

On special occasions, women courtiers wore hair cones made of animal fat scented with spices and herbs.

Discover more interesting facts about ancient Egypt

• The tomb of the pharaoh Tutankhamun was discovered complete in 1922 with a treasure of over 5000 objects. He was buried in the Valley of Kings in three separate coffins.

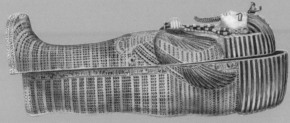

• Egyptian clothes were mainly made from light-coloured linen. Women wore long dresses. Men wore robes or kilt-like skirts. Clothes like these helped them stay cool in hot weather.

• The Egyptians were taken over by the Hyksos people from the east. The Hyksos brought the horse-drawn chariot into Egypt. The Egyptians copied the chariot and used it to defeat the Hyksos and drive them away!

The pharaoh quite often married a close relative, such as his sister or half-sister!

Rich people wore wigs made from human hair or sheep's wool, which they kept on special stands.

Bread was the most important food in the diet of ancient Egyptians. Their favourite drink was beer!

Fly swatters were made from giraffe tails! They were very popular fashion items in ancient Egypt.

Fun facts

Most ordinary people went barefoot because footwear was a luxury. Rich people wore padded leather sandals.

The most popular sport in ancient Egypt was hippo hunting – although it was very dangerous.

The base of the Great Pyramid is nearly as big as five football pitches!

Test your memory!

How much can you remember from your ancient Egypt sticker activity book? Find out below!

1. What is Egyptian writing called?
2. Whose death mask was found in the Valley of Kings?
3. What was Sobek the god of?
4. Who did the pharaoh often marry?
5. How long did the Great Pyramid take to build?
6. Which pyramids are the oldest?
7. How many children did Ramses II have?
8. Which pharaoh ruled for over 60 years?
9. What was the name of the king of the gods?
10. Who did Queen Cleopatra VII marry?
11. What weapons did soldiers use?
12. How did Egyptians make ink?

Bulbs of garlic were used to scare away snakes and to get rid of tapeworms from inside people's bodies.

13. What was placed on the face of a mummy?

14. How many hieroglyphics were there?

15. When did the river Nile flood the land?

16. What guards the Great Pyramid?

17. Who kept daily written records of everything that happened?

18. What were fly swatters made from?

19. Was the pharaoh important?

20. What was the most popular sport?

Answers:

1. Hieroglyphics 2. Tutankhamun's 3. The river Nile
4. His sister or half-sister 5. Over 20 years 6. Step
pyramids 7. 96 boys and 60 girls 8. Ramses II
9. Amun-Ra 10. Mark Anthony 11. Metal spears and
wooden shields 12. Using water with soot, charcoal or
coloured minerals 13. A death mask 14. 700 15. Between
July and November 16. The Great Sphinx 17. A scribe
18. Giraffe tails 19. Yes, the pharaoh was the most
important person 20. Hippo hunting

Bricks for Egyptian houses were made from a mixture of mud, straw and stones. They were shaped into bricks and left out in the sun to dry.

At his funeral, a magnificent boat, over 43 metres long, carried the body of King Khufu.

Robbers used to steal everything from tombs – even the dead body!

A special book for tomb robbers called 'The Book of Buried Pearls' gave details of all the hidden treasures.

Wordsearch

Can you find the words listed on the left, hidden in the wordsearch below?

AMULET

HIEROGLYPH

MUMMY

NILE

PAPYRUS

PHARAOH

PYRAMID

SCRIBE

SPHINX

P	O	M	U	M	M	Y	D	H	S
A	M	U	L	E	T	Z	N	L	P
P	S	P	Y	R	A	M	I	D	H
Y	R	W	H	E	P	G	L	K	I
R	Y	N	T	A	I	B	F	C	N
U	D	I	G	U	R	E	N	Y	X
S	A	L	N	R	O	A	H	L	K
E	D	E	Y	B	M	T	O	Q	F
S	C	R	I	B	E	C	T	H	G
H	I	E	R	O	G	L	Y	P	H

ANCIENT ROME

AUGUSTUS

JULIUS

SPARTACUS

CLAUDIUS

Introduction

About 2000 years ago, Rome was the most powerful city in the world. It began as a village of wooden huts, but grew and grew until over one million people lived there.

The ancient Romans are famous for their impressive buildings and new inventions. They built forts, roads and new towns.

With this great sticker book you can learn all about life in ancient Rome and amaze your friends with historical knowledge.

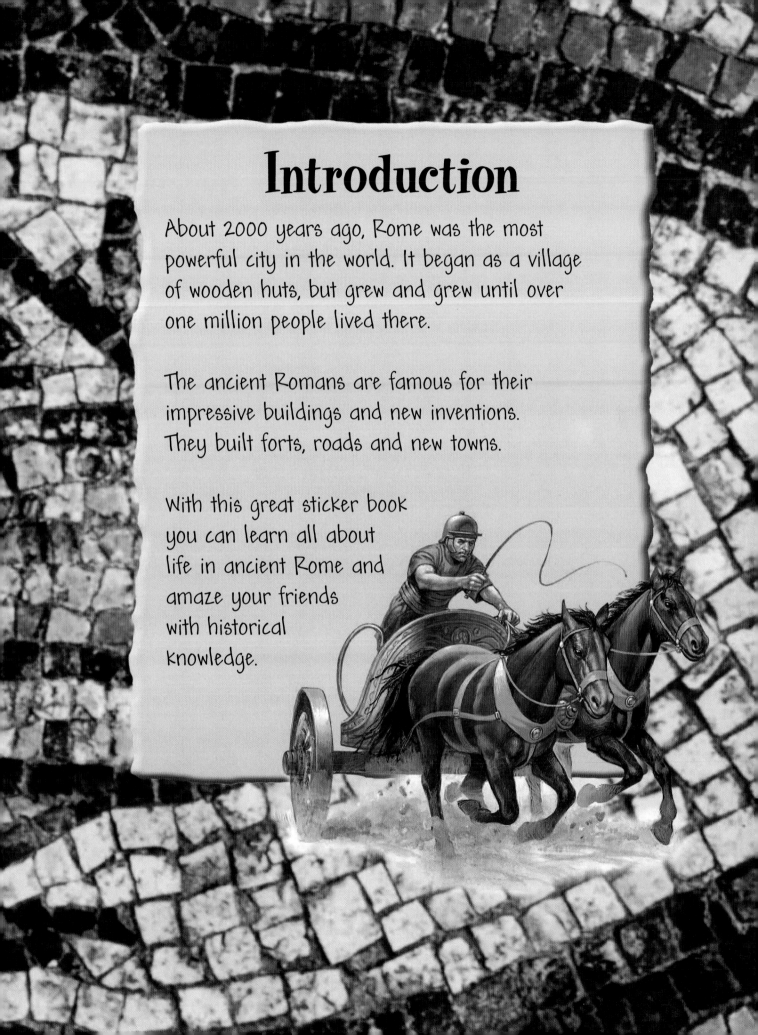

Mini stickers!

 Who fought in front of thousands of fans? Where did the Romans go to relax? Use your mini stickers to learn all about Roman life!

Life in ancient Rome – Romans went to school and had jobs just like we do today

Battle – Rome's army helped to build the impressive Roman empire

Gladiators – Romans went to a huge stadium called the Colosseum to watch gladiators do battle

Architecture – The ancient Romans built many very big and impressive structures, some of which still stand today

Leisure – Romans were interested in fashion, art and games

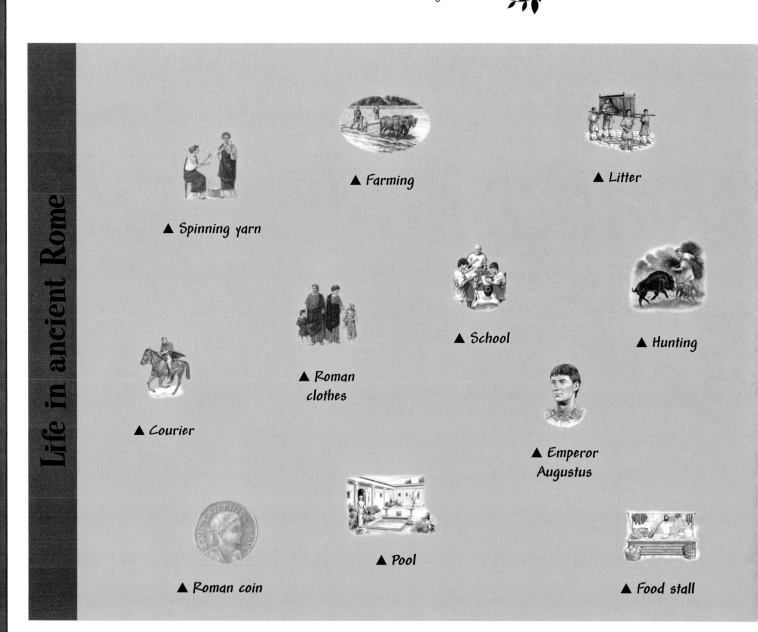

Life in ancient Rome

▲ Spinning yarn

▲ Farming

▲ Litter

▲ School

▲ Hunting

▲ Roman clothes

▲ Courier

▲ Emperor Augustus

▲ Pool

▲ Roman coin

▲ Food stall

Battle

▲ Queen Boudicca

▲ Soldier

▲ Warship

▲ Standard bearer

▲ Testudo

▲ Fort

Gladiators

▲ Gladiators fighting

▲ Name scroll

▲ Wild tiger

▲ Gladiator helmet

Architecture

▲ The Colosseum

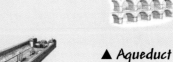
▲ Aqueduct

▲ Temple of Claudius

▲ The Circus Maximus

Leisure time

▲ Busker

▲ Banquet

▲ Music

▲ Mosaic

▲ Roman baths

▲ Games

▲ Chariot racing

Ancient Rome

 ◀ **Spinning yarn**

Women spun yarn on a spindle and then wove it into woollen fibre for making cloth

▶ **Gladiators fighting**

Romans watched gladiators battle against each other in stadiums

▼ **Warship**

The Roman army travelled across the sea on large ships, looking for new lands to conquer

▲ **Farming**

The Romans raised cattle and used oxen to help plough the fields, ready for new crops

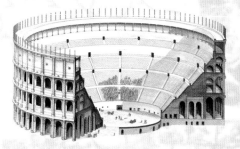

▲ **The Colosseum**

Gladiators fought each other in the huge stadium called the Colosseum, which seated over 50,000 people

▼ **Food stall**

Only rich Roman people had their own kitchens, ordinary people bought cooked snacks from roadside stalls

▲ **Roman baths**

The Romans went to the public baths to get clean, relax, have a massage and meet friends

▲ **Emperor Augustus**

In 27 BC an army general called Octavian brought peace to Rome and became the very first emperor – he renamed himself Augustus

KEY:

 Life in ancient Rome   Battle Gladiators   Architecture   Leisure

◄ Soldier
Roman soldiers had to march long distances carrying heavy weapons and armour

 ► Music
Romans enjoyed being entertained by troops of musicians and dancers

▼ Wild tiger
Gladiators had to fight fierce wild beasts such as tigers, as well as each other

▲ Aqueduct
Romans designed raised channels called aqueducts to carry water from faraway streams into the city

 ▼ Courier
Couriers were official messengers who rode on horseback and often travelled for long distances

► Mosaic
Mosaics are pictures built up from thousands of small tiles – this mosaic may have been designed for the floor of a bathhouse

 ◄ Chariot racing
Fast, exciting chariot races were held in a stadium called the Circus Maximus

◄ School
Boys went to school from the age of seven and were taught reading and writing

Roman soldiers guarding the cold northern frontiers of Britain kept warm by wearing short woollen trousers, like underpants, beneath their tunics!

Banquet fun!

Most Romans ate very little during the day. They had bread and water for breakfast and a light snack of bread, cheese or fruit for lunch. They ate their main meal about 4 pm. In rich people's homes, a meal would have three separate courses, and could last for up to three hours!

Romans ate lying down at parties. Men and women lay on long couches arranged round a table. They also often wore crowns of flowers, and took off their sandals before entering the dining room.

Make a Roman pendant

You will need:
• scissors • thread or wool
• card • paint • paintbrush

1. For the chain, cut the thread or wool to the right length for your own neck.
2. For the pendant, cut out a disc of card.
3. Paint a design on the card. It could be a dolphin or perhaps a scary monster called a gorgon, with a woman's face but tangled hair full of snakes.
4. Make a hole near the top of the disc and thread the 'chain' through it.

▼ Dishes served at a Roman banquet might include shellfish, roast meat, eggs, vegetables, fresh fruits, pastries and honeyed wine. The Romans enjoyed spicy food and sweet-sour flavours.

Ancient Rome

▲ Spinning yarn

▲ Food stall

▲ Gladiators fighting

▲ Emperor Augustus

▲ Roman baths

▲ The Colosseum

▲ Warship

▲ Farming

▼ Spinning yarn

► Food stall

◄ Gladiators fighting

▼ Emperor Augustus

▼ Roman baths

◄ The Colosseum

▼ Farming

▲ Warship

Ancient Rome

▲ Mosaic

▲ Aqueduct

▲ Soldier

▲ Music

▲ Courier

▲ Wild tiger

▲ School

▲ Chariot racing

◄ Mosaic

▲ Aqueduct

► Soldier

◄ Music

► Courier

▲ Courier

▼ Wild tiger

▲ School

► Chariot racing

▼ Roman clothes

► Pool

► The Circus
Maximus

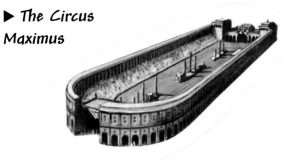

▼ Hunting

► Busker

▼ Litter

▼ Testudo

▲ Gladiator helmet

▲ Roman clothes

▲ Pool

▲ The Circus Maximus

▲ Hunting

▲ Busker

▲ Litter

▲ Gladiator helmet

▲ Testudo

Ancient Rome

▲ Temple of Claudius

▲ Roman coin

◀ Standard bearer

▼ Banquet

▲ Queen Boudicca

▼ Fort

▼ Games

AUGUSTUS
JULIUS
SPARTACUS
CLAUDIUS

▲ Name scroll

▲ Temple of Claudius

▲ Roman coin

▲ Standard bearer

▲ Banquet

▲ Queen Boudicca

▲ Fort

▲ Games

▲ Name scroll

Gladiator school!

Gladiators attended a special school called a ludos. Here they were taught to fight. They practised with wooden weapons so that they were not hurt during training. New gladiators fought against a wooden post called a palus. Only when they had learnt the basic moves were they allowed to practise against other gladiators.

Once the gladiators were trained, many were sent to fight in the Colosseum to entertain the people of Rome. They sometimes fought in teams, or by themselves, and sometimes against fierce wild animals. The people of Rome watched these brutal fights as often as we watch football games now.

◀ Gladiators trained for several hours every day. They were taught fighting techniques by retired gladiators.

Ancient Rome

◄ **Roman clothes**

Romans wore loose-fitting robes called togas. Purple dye was expensive, so wearing purple-coloured cloth was a sign of wealth

▲ **Pool**

Pools were built for decoration in the courtyards of large homes

► **Testudo**

Soldiers used their shields to make a protective shell – this was called a testudo, which means 'tortoise'

▼ **The Circus Maximus**

This was a famous race track where Romans watched chariot racing

▲ **Hunting**

Romans hunted wild boar for food

▲ **Gladiator helmet**

Some gladiators wore helmets with no eye holes – this added to the excitement for the spectators

◄ **Busker**

Groups of buskers played music in the street, or were hired for private parties

◄ **Litter**

Rich Romans were carried along in curtained beds called litters

KEY:  Life in ancient Rome   Battle   Gladiators   Architecture   Leisure

▼ **Queen Boudicca**
Boudicca was a British queen who led a rebellion against the Roman empire, but she was defeated

 ▶ **Name scroll**
Before a show, the names of the gladiators who were going to fight were written on a scroll

 ▼ **Roman coin**
Roman coins featured a picture of the emperor who was in power

 ◀ **Temple of Claudius**
When emperor Claudius died the Romans built an impressive temple in his honour

 ▶ **Fort**
The Roman army built well-protected forts to defend themselves from attack

 ▶ **Games**
Romans played games with boards made of pottery and pieces of bone, glass or clay

 ◀ **Standard bearer**
The standard bearer led the Roman troops into battle

 ◀ **Banquet**
Rich Romans enjoyed lots of different foods such as roast meats, fresh fruit and vegetables

One Roman emperor was mad! Emperor Nero was said to have laughed and played music while watching a terrible fire destroy most of Rome.

Fun facts

Odd jobs!

Couriers travelled so quickly that they had to stop at inns along the way to swap their worn out horses for new ones.

Roman engineers designed public lavatories. They weren't very private though – all the people sat on seats next to each other!

Roman theatre actors were almost all men, and some were so popular that they had big groups of fans.

Read on to find out about some of the different jobs people had in Roman times

• Rome had its own fire brigade. The 7000 firemen were all specially trained.

• Roman engineers used tools to help them make careful plans and take detailed measurements before starting any new building project.

• Going to the barbers could be very painful! In Roman times sharp scissors and razors had not been invented. Instead barbers used shears to trim hair and beards.

Poor Romans were given free bread by the government. In one month in 44 BC, over 330,000 men queued to receive this free food.

No place like Rome!

Discover more about life in Rome

• Actors in ancient Rome wore masks with big, bold face expressions. This allowed the audience, even those at the back, to see if the character was happy or sad.

• Fruit trees were planted around many Roman villas and were carefully looked after through the seasons.

• Romans wore togas. These were large pieces of cloth that were folded and draped around the body, and then fastened with a brooch.

Many Roman mosaics have been discovered accidentally, and have been carefully dug up.

The Romans invented Valentine's Day, but called it Lupercalia. Boys picked a girl's name from a hat, and she had to be their girlfriend for the whole year.

Although the Romans liked bathing, they only visited the baths once every nine days.

The Romans often consulted a fortune-teller or priest before setting out on a long journey!

Fun facts

Gladiator helmets were very heavy – they weighed about 7 kilograms, twice as much as an army helmet.

Romans loved watching animals that had been trained to perform. One animal trainer put on shows where an ape drove a chariot pulled by camels!

Children's toys in ancient Rome included dolls, toy chariots, marbles and dice.

Test your memory!

How much can you remember from your ancient Rome sticker activity book?
Find out below!

1. What was the name of the huge stadium where chariot racing took place?
2. Who was the very first Roman emperor?
3. Where did Romans go to get clean?
4. How many spectators did the Colosseum seat?
5. What were aqueducts used for?
6. How did couriers deliver their messages so quickly?
7. How old were Roman boys when they first went to school?
8. What was the name of the tool that yarn was spun on?
9. How did Romans eat at parties?
10. What was the name of the special school that gladiators attended?

Yummy dishes for a Roman banquet might include eels, thrushes, dormice, bear cutlets, sow's udders and even poached snails!

Fun facts

11. What was the name of the loose-fitting clothes that many Romans wore?
12. Who was the British queen who led a rebellion against the Romans?
13. What did a standard bearer do?
14. What was special about purple togas?
15. What happened before a gladiator show?
16. What did Roman actors wear on stage?
17. What was strange about Roman face make-up?
18. How often did Romans visit the public baths?
19. How heavy was a gladiator helmet?
20. Which Roman emperor was said to have laughed and played music as he watched a terrible fire destroy Rome?

Answers:

1. Circus Maximus 2. Emperor Augustus
3. The public baths 4. 50,000 5. Transporting water
6. They travelled on horseback 7. Seven years old 8. Spindle
9. They ate lying down 10. Ludos 11. Togas
12. Queen Boudicca 13. He led troops into battle
14. They were expensive 15. The gladiators' names were read out
16. They wore masks 17. It was made from poisonous lead
18. Every nine days 19. About 7 kilograms 20. Emperor Nero

Roman women wore make-up. Their face powder was made from chalk or even lead, which was poisonous!

Julius Caesar is the most famous Roman emperor. He was betrayed and murdered by people he thought were his friends.

The Romans sometimes used elephants to trample the enemy in battle!

Roman ships have been preserved in the mud of the river Thames in London. Archaeologists have also discovered tools and pottery.

Wordsearch

Can you find the words listed on the left, hidden in the wordsearch below?

ARMY

AQUEDUCT

BATHS

CHARIOT

COLOSSEUM

EMPEROR

GLADIATOR

SOLDIER

TESTUDO

C	O	L	O	S	S	E	U	M	O
F	G	E	C	O	P	L	M	E	K
A	S	L	H	R	W	A	B	M	U
Q	L	P	A	O	G	R	D	P	S
U	T	U	R	D	R	M	M	E	O
E	R	I	I	J	I	Y	V	R	L
D	Q	A	O	C	D	A	K	O	D
U	B	A	T	H	S	G	T	R	I
C	F	N	Y	S	L	I	O	O	E
T	E	S	T	U	D	O	T	N	R

VIKINGS

Introduction

The Vikings lived in Scandinavia over 1000 years ago. Viking warriors were famous for their bravery and violence. They battled to win new lands and gradually spread through Europe.

Viking explorers travelled far and wide, and set up new villages in Iceland, Greenland and Russia. They were the very first people from Europe to discover North America in AD 1000.

With this great sticker book you can learn all about life as a Viking. Discover which king was famous for his cruelty and how Vikings settled arguments. Then impress your friends with amazing facts!

Mini stickers!

Who were the great Viking warriors? How did Vikings bathe? Which stories did Vikings like to tell? Use your mini stickers to learn all about Vikings and their daily life.

Battles and warriors – Vikings were famous for their bravery

Kings – At the head of Viking society were kings or chiefs

Viking life – In their spare time Vikings relaxed with games and sports

Gods – Vikings worshipped many different gods and goddesses

Legends – Vikings loved telling exciting stories and hearing about magical tales

Battles and warriors

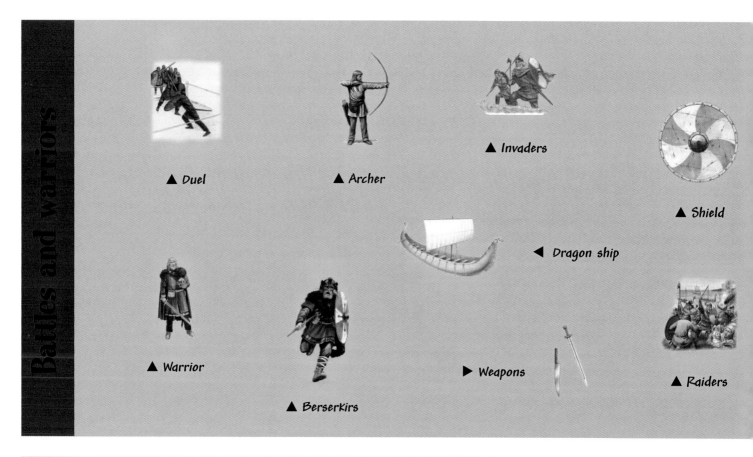

▲ Duel

▲ Archer

▲ Invaders

▲ Shield

◄ Dragon ship

▲ Warrior

▲ Berserkirs

► Weapons

▲ Raiders

Kings

▲ Erik Bloodaxe

▲ King Cnut

▲ Sigurd the Stout

▲ Farming

▲ Pots

▼ Mealtime

▲ Making clothes

▲ Feeding chickens

◄ Games

▲ Longhouse

▼ Mother and child

▲ Sauna

▲ Toilet

▲ Boys playing

---

ds

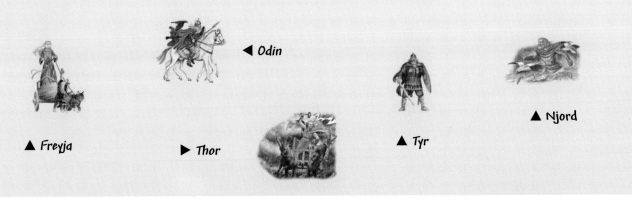

▲ Freyja

◄ Odin

► Thor

▲ Tyr

▲ Njord

Legends

► Ragnarok

▲ Lucky charm

▲ Storytelling

◄ Valkyrie

Life as a Viking

 ▶ Duel

Viking warriors challenged
people who insulted them,
or their families, to
a deadly duel

▶ Lucky charm

This is a Viking lucky
charm that is shaped like
Thor's hammer

◀ Freyja

The Viking goddess
Freyja rode in a
chariot pulled by cats

▶ Weapons

Many warriors gave
their swords names as
they were their most
treasured possession

▼ Archer

Viking archers used bows made of
yew wood and twisted plant fibres

▶ Sigurd the Stout

Sigurd the Stout believed that
whoever carried his flag was
sure of victory for his army –
but would die himself

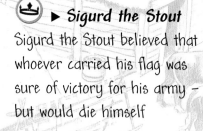

◀ Pots

Vikings used pots made from pottery
and silver for cooking, and drank
from hollowed-out cattle horns

▶ Longhouse

Viking longhouses were large
enough for the family's
animals to live in too

KEY:

 Battles and warriors

 Kings

 Viking life

 Gods

Legends

▼ **Invaders**

Vikings invaded new lands and made settlements, and claimed the land for their own

 ▲ **Farming**

The Vikings realized that the British Isles provided good farmland and safe areas to live

 ◄ **Shield**

This round shield is made of wood and covered with leather

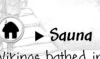 ► **Sauna**

Vikings bathed in clouds of steam– very similar to saunas– which are still popular today

 ◄ **Odin**

Odin was the Viking god of war – he rode an eight-legged horse

 ▼ **Warrior**

Viking warriors were famous for their bravery and violence

 ▼ **Games**

This board and counters were probably used to play the game 'hneftafl' – which is like chess

 ▼ **Ragnarok**

Viking legends told stories of how the world was going to end – at the battle of Ragnarok

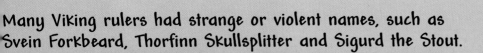

Many Viking rulers had strange or violent names, such as Svein Forkbeard, Thorfinn Skullsplitter and Sigurd the Stout.

Viking vessels

Vikings were brave adventurers who were keen to seek out new lands. Viking longboats were fast and could travel far across open seas. They were made from long planks fitted onto wooden frames. Vikings carefully watched and kept note of the position of the stars and Sun to navigate (find their way) at sea. Viking explorers used these longboats to reach America about 1000 years ago.

Sails were invented at least 5000 years ago. Vikings used both sails and oars – this helped them to travel quickly.

Vikings

▲ Duel

▲ Archer

▲ Weapons

▲ Sigurd the Stout

▲ Pots

▲ Longhouse

▲ Lucky charm

▲ Freyja

▲ Duel

▲ Sigurd the Stout

▶ Archer

◀ Weapons

▲ Pots

◀ Longhouse

▶ Lucky charm

▲ Freyja

Vikings

▲ Invaders

▲ Shield

▲ Warrior

▲ Farming

▲ Games

▲ Sauna

▲ Odin

▲ Ragnarok

◀ Invaders

▲ Farming

▶ Warrior

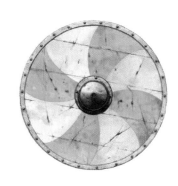

▶ Shield

▶ Sauna

◀ Games

▼ Odin

▼ Ragnarok

◄ Berserkirs

▼ Making clothes

► Erik Bloodaxe

▼ Feeding chickens

▲ Mother and child

◄ Toilet

► Tyr

▼ Valkyrie

▲ Berserkirs

▲ Making clothes

▲ Erik Bloodaxe

▲ Feeding chickens

▲ Mother and child

▲ Toilet

▲ Tyr

▲ Valkyrie

Vikings

▲ Dragon ship

▼ King Cnut

▲ Raiders

▲ Mealtime

▼ Boys playing

▶ Thor

▼ Njord

▲ Storytelling

▲ Dragon ship

▲ Raiders

▲ King Cnut

▲ Mealtime

▲ Thor

▲ Boys playing

▲ Njord

▲ Storytelling

Deadly duel!

Vikings followed a strict code of honour. Men and women were dignified and proud, and honour was very important to them. It was a disgrace to be called a cheat or a coward, or to run away from a fight. Vikings also prized loyalty. They swore solemn promises to be faithful to lords and comrades and sealed bargains by shaking hands.

Make a Viking pendant

You will need:
- string • modelling clay
- white and yellow paint • paintbrush

1. Shape some animal fangs from modelling clay.
2. Make a hole at the widest part of the fang.
3. Paint the fangs white and yellow.
4. Thread string through the fangs and wear around your neck like a Viking.

Quarrels between Viking families led to feuds. These could continue for many months, with many people on both sides being killed.

Life as a Viking

 ◄ Berserkirs

Berserkir warriors rushed madly into battle-wearing animal skins and chain-mail armour

◄ Making clothes

Viking women spun sheep's wool and wove it into warm cloth on tall, upright looms

► Erik Bloodaxe

Erik Bloodaxe was famous for his cruelty – he was the last Viking to rule north-east England

▼ Feeding chickens

Feeding chickens was work for Viking girls – they learnt how to grow vegetables and cook by helping their mother

► Tyr

Tyr was a fierce god who Vikings asked to help them win victories

▲ Toilet

Viking toilets may have looked like this – they used dry moss, grass or leaves as toilet paper

► Mother and child

Viking women made important household decisions, cooked, cleaned, made clothes and raised the children

▲ Valkyrie

Vikings believed that Valkyries were wild warrior women who carried men who had died in battle to live with Odin in the hall of the brave dead

KEY:

 Battles and warriors

 Kings

 Viking life

Gods

 Legends

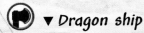 **▼ Dragon ship**
Viking dragon ships were long and sleek, made from overlapping planks of wood, held together with iron nails

 ▲ Storytelling
Vikings loved telling each other sagas – stories that recorded past events and famous people's lives

► King Cnut
King Cnut ruled a large empire but didn't want to look too proud, so he tried to control the sea, even though he knew he would fail

► Thor
Vikings believed that Thor was the god of storms and that he could control the Universe with his hammer

 **◄ Boys playing**
Viking boys practised fighting with swords made from wood and small, light shields

► Raiders
Loyal warriors were sent on journeys – they sailed away from their homes to attack villages so that they could steal their valuables

► Njord
Vikings believed that Njord was the god of the sea – he married the giantess, Skadi, who watched over mountains

▲ Mealtime
Viking women and slaves cooked huge meals over open fires – and served them to feasting warriors

Vikings liked living in longhouses because heat from the animals provided a kind of central heating that kept everyone warm.

Viking facts

Vikings believed that after Ragnarok a new world would be born.

Viking longhouses were usually built on sloping ground so that animal waste ran down the hill!

If a Viking man wanted to marry he had to ask the woman's father for permission – if permission was granted the marriage would go ahead.

Victorious Vikings!

Read on to find out about some ancient record-breaking facts

• Each Viking soldier had to provide his own weapons and armour. Wealthy Vikings could afford metal helmets and tunics, and sharp swords.

• Vikings made long journeys across land in winter because the frozen ground was easier to walk across with heavy loads.

• Every year Vikings met at the Thing. This was an open-air assembly of all men in the area. It met to punish criminals and make new laws.

Viking men wore make-up! They particularly liked eyeliner – probably made from soot.

Discover more interesting facts about Vikings

• The Vikings believed that runes – their way of writing – had magic healing powers. Runes were written on women's palms during childbirth to protect them from pain.

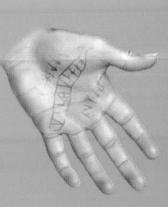

• Viking men and women liked to wear brightly patterned clothes. They often decorated their clothes with strips of woven braid.

• Viking children did not go to school. Daughters helped their mothers with cooking and cleaning, fed farm animals, and learned to spin, weave and sew. Sons helped their fathers in the workshop or on the farm.

Vikings believed that two ravens called Thought and Memory flew alongside Odin – the god of war.

Viking men and women wore lots of jewellery, partly to show how wealthy they were.

If a Viking was injured in the stomach, then he was made to eat onions. If his comrades could smell onions from his wound they knew it was bad!

The Vikings imported boatloads of broken glass from Germany, to melt into beautiful glass beads.

Test your memory!

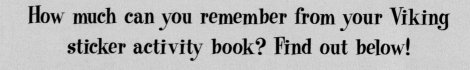

Berserkir warriors rushed madly into battle, chewing their shields and growling like wolves – this was done to scare enemies.

Viking warriors' swords were their most treasured possession – they would sometimes even give them a special name!

Vikings loved riddles and even liked to play practical jokes on each other.

How much can you remember from your Viking sticker activity book? Find out below!

1. What did Vikings use as a painkiller?
2. What did Vikings decorate their clothes with?
3. What was the Thing?
4. What did Vikings drink from?
5. What was Viking eyeliner made from?
6. When did Viking women start to knot their hair?
7. What did Vikings make from broken glass?
8. What did Vikings believe flew beside the god Odin?
9. If a Viking was injured in the stomach what was he made to eat?
10. What was the name of the Viking goddess who rode in a chariot pulled by cats?

Viking women went to war but they did not fight! Instead, they nursed wounded warriors and cooked meals for hungry soldiers.

11. What did Sigurd the Stout believe would happen to anyone who carried his flag?
12. What was the name of the Viking god of war?
13. What did Vikings call the end of the world?
14. What did the god Odin ride on?
15. Vikings bathed in clouds of what?
16. What did Vikings believe the Valkyries did?
17. What was Njord the god of?
18. What did Vikings do when someone died?
19. What did King Cnut try, and fail to do?
20. What did Vikings believe it was a disgrace to run away from?

Answers:

1. Runes 2. Strips of woven braid 3. An open-air assembly 4. Hollowed out cattle horns 5. Soot 6. When they were married 7. Glass beads 8. Two ravens 9. Onions 10. Freyja 11. He believed they would die in battle 12. Odin 13. Ragnarok 14. An eight-legged horse 15. Steam 16. Carried warriors to live in the hall of the brave dead 17. The sea 18. Put their body on board a ship and set fire to it 19. To command the sea 20. A fight

A metal centre panel on the shield helped to protect the warrior's hand.

Viking women wore their hair long until they were married. They then tied it in a knot at the back of their neck.

When Vikings died, their bodies were placed on a ship that was set on fire so that their souls would sail away to the next world.

The Viking god Thor was said to have pretended to marry a giant who had stolen his magic hammer – Thor wanted to steal it back again!

Wordsearch

Can you find the words listed on the left,
hidden in the wordsearch below?

ARCHER

BERSERKIR

LONGBOAT

LONGHOUSE

RAIDER

SAUNA

SHIELD

THOR

WARRIOR

S	A	U	N	A	R	F	B	U	J
H	S	E	G	M	T	A	V	W	K
I	P	A	D	U	Y	H	R	A	L
E	L	R	N	R	I	W	O	R	O
L	D	C	F	A	Z	W	U	R	N
D	V	H	Q	I	G	E	K	I	G
I	C	E	F	D	M	G	A	O	B
B	E	R	S	E	R	K	I	R	O
S	N	H	B	R	E	T	J	A	A
L	O	N	G	H	O	U	S	E	T

KNIGHTS & CASTLES

Introduction

Castles were once magnificent homes to kings and lords and their brave fighting knights. Fierce battles often took place to defend the great castles, and knights in armour risked their lives to protect them. Many castles still stand today and you could visit some of them to discover more.

With this great sticker book you can learn about different kinds of knights and castles and amaze your friends with fun facts!

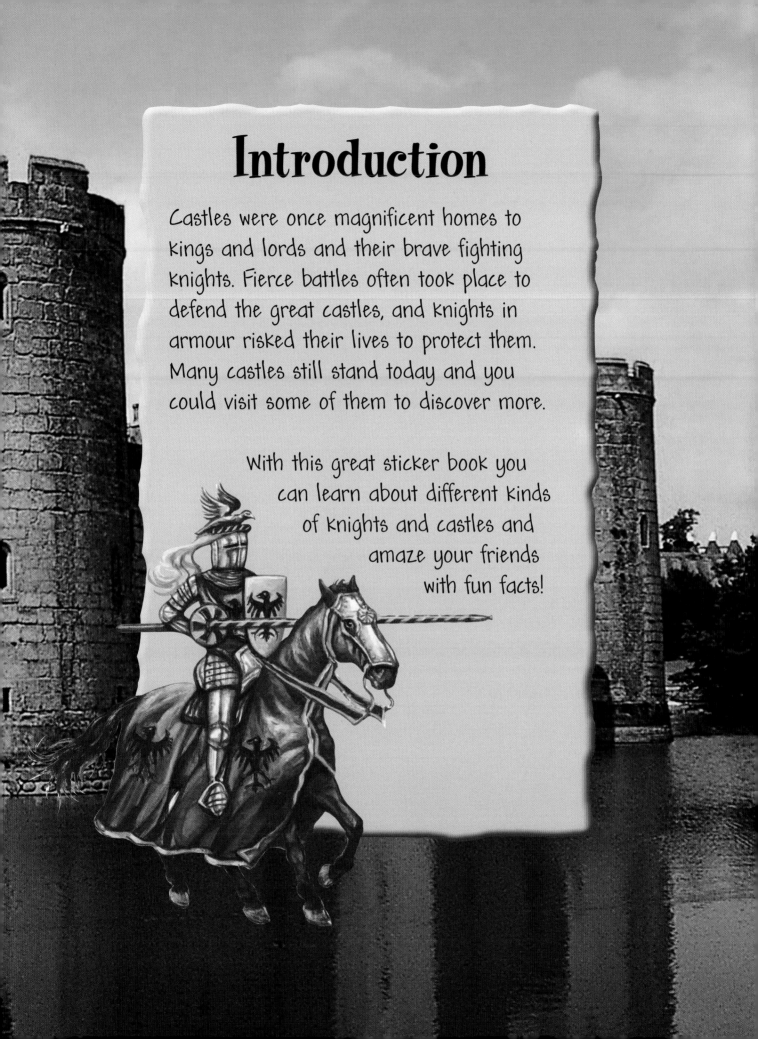

Mini stickers!

What weapons did knights use in battle and at tournaments? Why were castles so cold? What was the code of chivalry? Use your mini stickers to learn all about castles and the knights who defended them.

Knights – skilled soldiers who rode into battle on horseback
Castles – large buildings with towers and battlements, used as fortresses
Weapons – items such as swords and crossbows used at tournaments and in battle
Banners/Shields – used by knights to proudly display their colours and emblems

Knights

▲ Warrior Knight

▲ Knight in armour

▲ Foot combat

▲ Knight and lady

▲ Plate armour

▲ Saracen Knight

▲ Knight and warhorse

▲ Horseback fight

▲ Knight ready for battle

▲ Jousting Knight

▲ English Knight

▲ Knight of St John

▲ Fighting Knights

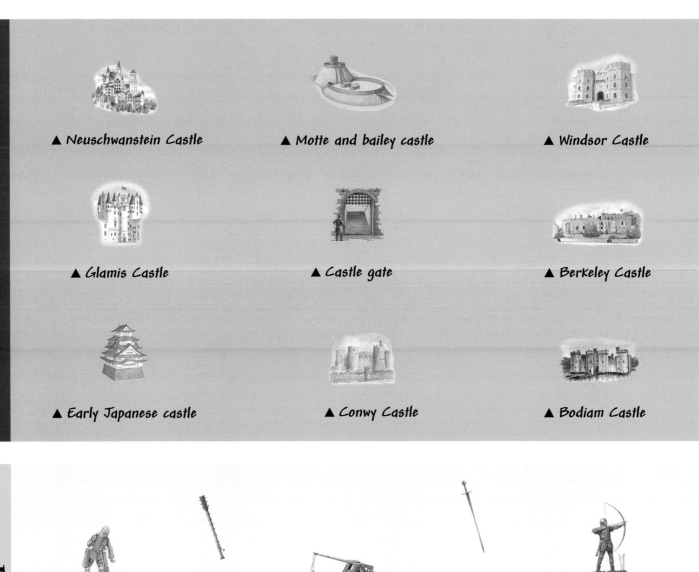

▲ Neuschwanstein Castle

▲ Motte and bailey castle

▲ Windsor Castle

▲ Glamis Castle

▲ Castle gate

▲ Berkeley Castle

▲ Early Japanese castle

▲ Conwy Castle

▲ Bodiam Castle

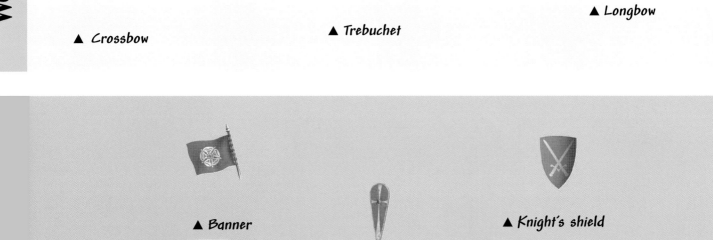

▲ Mace

▲ Sword

▲ Longbow

▲ Crossbow

▲ Trebuchet

▲ Banner

▲ Knight's shield

▲ Battle shield

▲ Shield

▲ Knight's flag

Knights and castles

(🏰) ◄ **Conwy Castle**
English monarch Edward I
built this castle in Wales
between 1283 and 1289

(🐎) ► **English Knight**
This English Knight is
ready to fight for the
honour of his country

(🛡) ▲ **Knight's flag**
Flags showed the knight's
colours and coat of arms

(⚔) ▲ **Trebuchet**
This massive rock-hurling weapon
was used to attack castles

(🛡) ▲ **Knight's shield**
Decorated shields were
used by knights as
protection during battle

(⚔) ◄ **Sword**
A sharp double-edged
blade was used in
battle and during
tournament fights

(🐎) ▲ **Jousting Knight**
In a jousting competition knights
carried a shield and lance

(🐎) ▲ **Foot combat**
This was a fight between
two knights at a tournament

KEY:

Knights

Castles

Weapons

Banners/Shields

▶ Berkeley Castle
Built between 1117 and 1153,
this castle is said to be haunted
by the ghost of Edward II

▲ Saracen Knight
These skilled Muslim archers
fought in the crusades – religious
wars during the Middle Ages

▼ Castle gate
Castle gates often had a heavy
grate, called a portcullis, to provide
an extra defence barrier

▲ Early Japanese castle
By the 1500s the Japanese
were building strong castles

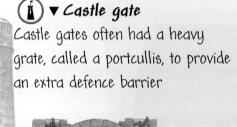

◀ Plate armour
By the 1400s, plate
armour covered the
knight's whole body

▼ Knight ready for battle
This knight is in full battle armour,
carrying his sword and shield

▲ Neuschwanstein Castle
King Ludwig of Bavaria started
building this fairytale castle in 1869

▲ Battle shield
A tall, narrow shield
used in battle

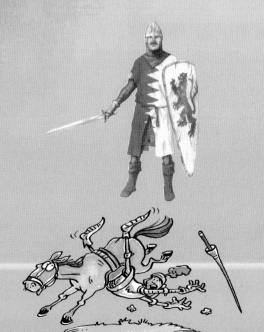

Some knights cheated in jousts by fixing their armour
onto the horse's saddle!

Preparing for battle

Special tournaments were held for knights to help them prepare for proper battles. In a tournament, knights took part in an event called jousting. This involved knights charging at each other at top speed on their horses. The aim was to knock your opponent off his horse with a blow from a long wooden lance.

The knights were protected by armour and they also wore their own personal colours and carried shields. Competing in jousts also gave a knight the chance to prove himself in front of the woman he loved. Jousts were popular events, watched by ladies of the court as well as ordinary people.

The knights held a decorated shield for extra protection

A knight's horse wore matching colours

The wall or tilt helped keep the horses charging in a straight line

▲ Knight's flag

▲ Sword

▲ Conwy Castle

▲ English knight

▲ Knight's shield

▲ Jousting Knight

▲ Foot combat

▲ Trebuchet

Knights and castles

▲ Knight's flag

▼ Sword

▲ Conwy Castle

▲ English knight

◄ Jousting Knight

▲ Knight's shield

▲ Foot combat

▲ Trebuchet

▲ Neuschwanstein Castle

▲ Saracen Knight

▲ Battle shield

▲ Berkeley Castle

▲ Knight ready for battle

▲ Early Japanese castle

▲ Plate armour

▲ Castle gate

Knights and castles

▶ Saracen Knight

▲ Neuschwanstein Castle

▲ Berkeley Castle

▲ Battle shield

▶ Knight ready for battle

▲ Early Japanese castle

▲ Plate armour

▲ Castle gate

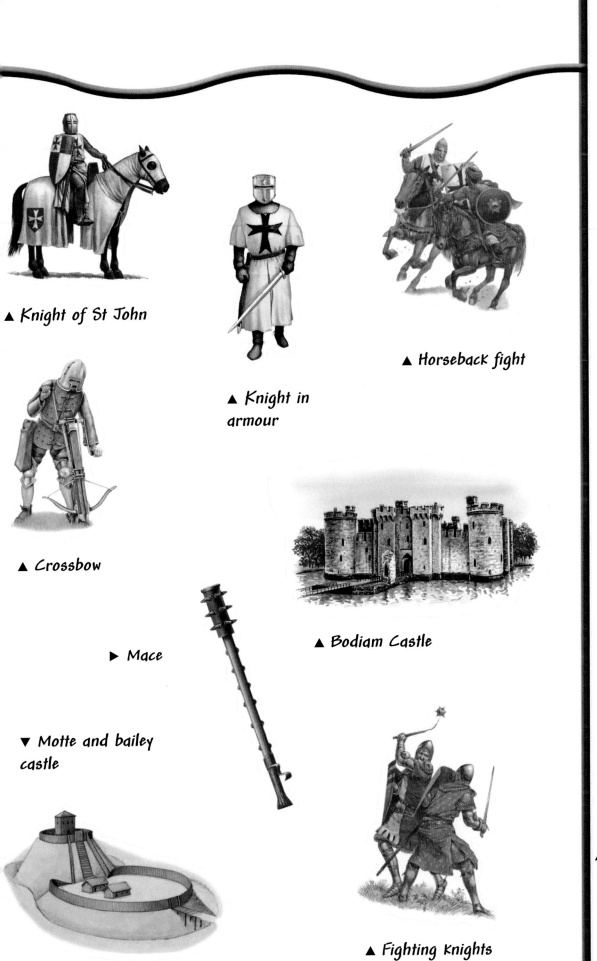

▲ Knight of St John

▲ Knight in armour

▲ Horseback fight

▲ Crossbow

▲ Bodiam Castle

▶ Mace

▼ Motte and bailey castle

▲ Fighting knights

▲ Knight of St John

▲ Knight in armour

▲ Horseback fight

▲ Crossbow

▲ Bodiam Castle

▲ Mace

▲ Motte and bailey castle

▲ Fighting knights

Knights and castles

◀ Shield

▶ Warrior Knight

▲ Knight and lady

▲ Windsor Castle

▲ Banner

▶ Longbow

▲ Knight and warhorse

▲ Glamis Castle

▲ Shield

▲ Warrior Knight

▲ Knight and lady

▲ Windsor Castle

▲ Banner

▲ Longbow

▲ Knight and warhorse

▲ Glamis Castle

Cold castles

Medieval stone castles were cold, damp places with lots of draughts. A castle was not exactly a luxury home. Cold winds blew through the windows, which had no glass, and there was no central heating or running water. Wool hangings and tapestries on the walls, and rugs on the floors helped to keep rooms warm. Roaring fires burned in the huge fireplaces.

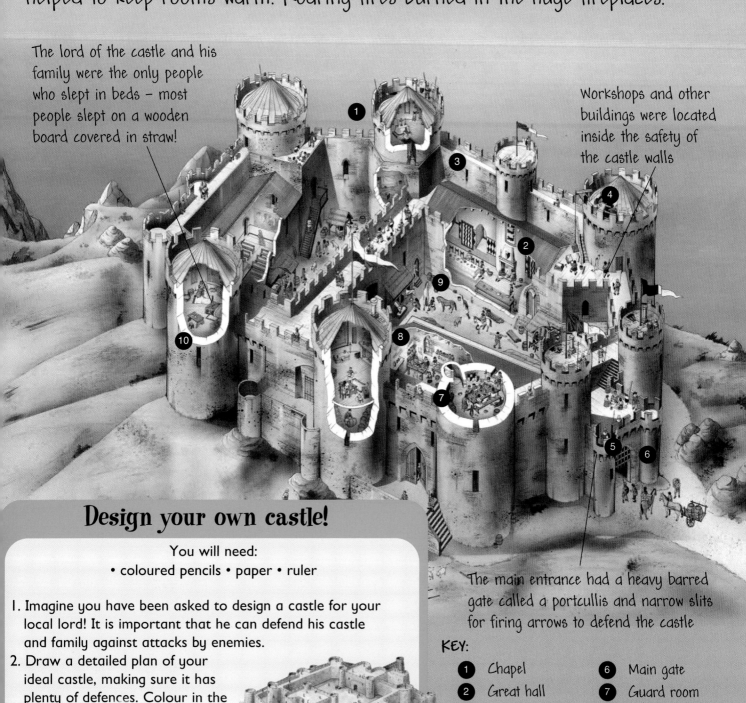

The lord of the castle and his family were the only people who slept in beds – most people slept on a wooden board covered in straw!

Workshops and other buildings were located inside the safety of the castle walls

The main entrance had a heavy barred gate called a portcullis and narrow slits for firing arrows to defend the castle

Design your own castle!

You will need:
• coloured pencils • paper • ruler

1. Imagine you have been asked to design a castle for your local lord! It is important that he can defend his castle and family against attacks by enemies.
2. Draw a detailed plan of your ideal castle, making sure it has plenty of defences. Colour in the different areas of use in the castle.

KEY:

1	Chapel	6	Main gate
2	Great hall	7	Guard room
3	Battlements	8	Kitchens
4	Prison tower	9	Stable
5	Portcullis	10	Royal tower

Knights and castles

▲ Knight of St John
Knights of this order lived like monks and followed very strict rules

▲ Knight in armour
This knight is wearing a protective helmet and patterned tunic

▲ Bodiam Castle
This moated castle is in southern England and it was built in the 1300s

◄ Mace
A club-shaped weapon used by knights in battle

◄ Fighting Knights
Two brave knights battle against each other

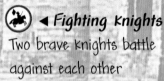

▼ Motte and bailey castle
This was a wooden castle built on a hilltop and surrounded by a wooden fence

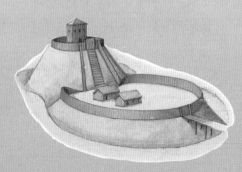

▼ Horseback fight
Crusader and Saracen knights often fought on horseback

▲ Crossbow
Crossbows fired arrows powerfully and accurately, but they were slow to reload

KEY:

Knights

Castles

Weapons

Banners/Shields

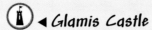 **◄ Glamis Castle**
Located in Scotland, this castle is the scene for the play *Macbeth* written by William Shakespeare

▼ Longbow
A skilled longbow archer could shoot an arrow up to 300 metres

 **▲ Windsor Castle**
Originally a wooden castle, the first stone buildings were added in the 1100s

▲ Shield
Shields carried the colours and patterns of the knight's lord

► Warrior Knight
Knights wore armour to protect themselves in battle

▼ Knight and lady
Knights were taught to follow strict rules about how to behave towards women

 **▲ Knight and warhorse**
Knights would normally have three horses – one for battle, one for riding and one for carrying loads

 **▲ Banner**
Banners were carried by knights to show loyalty to their lord

A crusader knight would share his tent with his beloved horse – it must have been a bit of a squeeze!

Fun facts

The biggest and best!

Knights wore personal colours and symbols during battles and tournaments. These became known as coats of arms.

Young boys started to learn how to be a knight at about the age of seven, when they were sent to serve as a page in a castle.

Castles often had no bathroom for the servants. They had to wash in the local river or stream.

Read on to find out some amazing facts about knights and castles

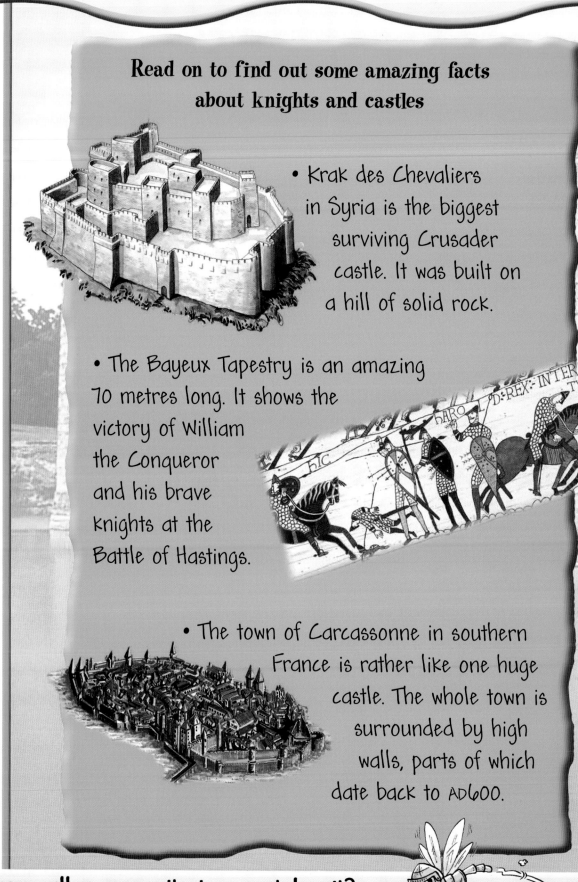

• Krak des Chevaliers in Syria is the biggest surviving Crusader castle. It was built on a hill of solid rock.

• The Bayeux Tapestry is an amazing 70 metres long. It shows the victory of William the Conqueror and his brave knights at the Battle of Hastings.

• The town of Carcassonne in southern France is rather like one huge castle. The whole town is surrounded by high walls, parts of which date back to AD600.

Q: What do you call a mosquito in a metal suit?
A: A bite in shining armour!

Knights and castles

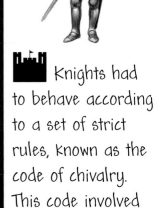

Discover more about brave knights and castle life

• The great hall was the centre of castle life. Large feasts of delicious food and wine were served as the lord and his guests were entertained by musicians, jesters, jugglers and acrobats.

• A knight would write secret letters to the woman he loved. They would also write poems to each other expressing their feelings of love and devotion.

• The legend of St George tells how he killed a fierce dragon. George saved the people of Lydia (part of modern Turkey) from the fire-breathing dragon.

Knights had to behave according to a set of strict rules, known as the code of chivalry. This code involved being brave and honourable in battle and at tournaments.

A knight who did not follow the code of chivalry was disgraced and punished.

Medieval castles had no proper toilets! Instead, people sat on wooden seats over a long chute. The waste dropped down into the moat!

Q: Why did the ponytailed knight visit his doctor?
A: He was a little hoarse!

Test your memory!

 Early knights wore a type of armour called chainmail. It was made of thousands of tiny iron rings joined together.

 Messengers called heralds carried messages between knights during battles.

 Japanese warrior knights in the Middles Ages were known as samurai. A long curving sword was a samurai's most treasured possession.

How much can you remember from your knights and castles sticker activity book? Find out below!

1. Which knight saved the people of Lydia by killing a fierce dragon?
2. Name the code which knights had to follow?
3. Which famous battle is featured on the Bayeux Tapestry?
4. Who started the building of Windsor Castle?
5. Did a knight's warhorse need to be small and lively or large and aggressive?
6. What was the name of the men who carried messages between knights during battles?
7. What name was given to Japanese warrior knights in the Middle Ages?
8. Is Beaumaris Castle in England, Scotland or Wales?
9. What room was the centre of castle life?
10. What was chainmail armour made from?

Q: Why did the King visit the dentist?
A: To get his teeth crowned!

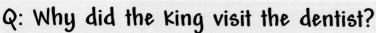

11. Who started the building of Neuschwanstein Castle?

12. Which castle is the scene for the play *Macbeth*?

13. How many metres could a skilled longbow archer shoot an arrow?

14. Which weapon was faster to reload: a crossbow or a longbow?

15. In what country is the Krak des Chevaliers Castle?

16. Name the massive rock-hurling weapon used to attack castles.

17. What was Windsor Castle orginally made from?

18. Which castle is said to be haunted by the ghost of Edward II?

19. Is a motte and bailey castle on a hilltop or in a dip?

20. What is a mace?

Answers:

1. St George 2. Code of chivalry 3. Battle of Hastings
4. William the Conqueror 5. Large and aggressive
6. Messengers 7. Samurai 8. Wales 9. The great hall
10. Thousands of tiny iron rings joined together
11. King Ludwig of Bavaria 12. Glamis Castle
13. Up to 300 metres 14. Longbow 15. Syria
16. Trebuchet 17. Wood 18. Berkeley Castle
19. On a hilltop 20. A club-shaped weapon

English kings and queens have lived at Windsor Castle since William the Conqueror started building it over 900 years ago.

Beaumaris Castle in Wales, was the last castle built by Edward I of England. He was the greatest castle builder of his day.

A knight's warhorse needed to be large and aggressive. These brave horses would often bite and kick the enemy in battle.

Q: What did the knight give to his coughing horse?
A: Cough stirrup!

Wordsearch

Can you find the words listed on the left,
hidden in the wordsearch below?

ARMOUR

BATTLE

CASTLE

CROSSBOW

KING

KNIGHT

LORD

SHIELD

SWORD

K	N	I	G	H	T	S	O	U	M
I	L	I	A	R	M	O	U	R	T
N	C	F	U	I	A	N	R	U	C
G	O	A	D	B	W	M	S	L	R
E	T	O	S	A	P	J	H	K	O
Z	S	V	B	T	G	S	I	D	S
L	W	I	U	T	L	Y	E	A	S
J	O	Y	F	L	S	E	L	E	B
I	R	R	Y	E	Q	P	D	R	O
O	D	K	D	C	V	R	A	L	W